Everyda

Illustrations by Maureen Bradley

A LITTLE LION

Thank you

Thank you for the world so sweet,
Thank you for the food we eat.
Thank you for the birds that sing,
Thank you, God, for everything.

Eating with a crowd

Bless this bunch
As we munch our lunch.

A harvest grace

All good gifts around us
Are sent from heaven above.
Then thank the Lord,
O thank the Lord
For all his love.

For simple meals

The bread is warm and fresh,
The water cool and clear.
Lord of all life, be with us,
Lord of all life, be near.

A grace to sing

For health and strength
and daily food,
we praise your name,
O Lord.

Thanks for all our food

For every cup and plateful,
God make us truly grateful.

A Jewish blessing

Blessed art thou, O Lord our God,
King of the Universe, who bringest
forth bread from the earth.

For food and drink

For food and drink and happy days,
Accept our gratitude and praise;
In serving others, Lord, we do
Express our thankfulness to you.

An invitation

Come, dear Lord Jesus, be our guest,
And bless what you have given us.

A Chinese grace

Each time we eat,
May we remember God's love.

God is great

God is great, God is good,
Thank you, God, for all our food.